Hit by a Blade

Contents

Written by Brian Beamer
Illustrated by Keith Olsen

Chapter 1

A Holiday with Grandad

Thu	Fri	Sat	Sun
2	3	4	5
9	10	11	12
16	17	18	19
23	24	25	26

fishing trip with Grandad.

Jessie and Juan lived where it was warm all year round. They loved the warm winters. They loved the hot, humid summers. They loved the sandy beaches and swimming in the warm water. But most of all they loved to go fishing.

Soon they would be going on a fishing trip with their grandad.

Jessie and Juan's grandad had a fishing boat. It was big enough to sleep on, and they would be gone for three days. They loved to sleep on their grandad's boat because he would tell them stories about when he was a boy. They would listen to his stories until the waves rocked them to sleep.

They packed their bags and told their friends they were going to catch some very big fish. The weather report was good, and they couldn't wait for the trip.

The night before they left, Grandad took out a map and spread it out on the table.

"Let's see where we'll be going," he said. "When we leave, we'll head out along the waterway to the open sea where the big fish live."

Jessie's eyes lit up with excitement. "How long will it take to get out to where the big fish live?" she asked.

"At least four hours," said Grandad.

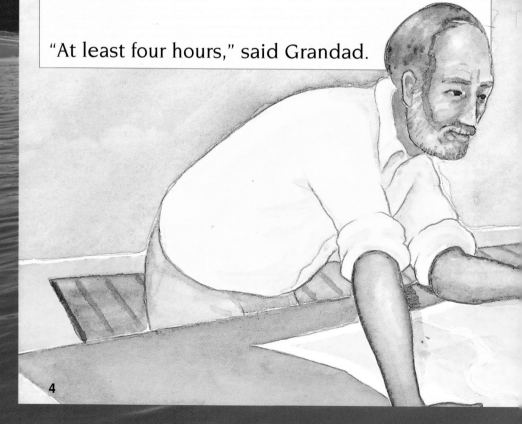

"Well you'd better get to bed," said Grandma. "Tomorrow is going to be a long day. You'll need lots of sleep if you're going to catch one of those big fish."

"Good night everyone," said Juan.

"See you in the morning," said Jessie. "I just know I'm going to catch the biggest fish."

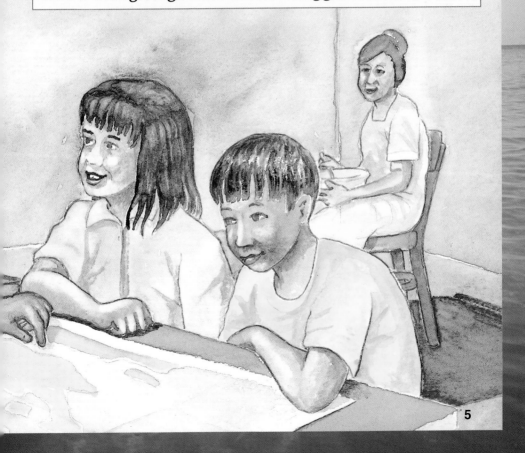

Chapter 2
Heading Out to Sea

Jessie and Juan were so excited they didn't need an alarm clock. Grandad had the car packed. They ate a quick breakfast and rushed out the door.

When they arrived, Grandad said, "Let's get everything on the boat. The sooner we get out to sea, the sooner we can start catching those big fish."

The weather was great and there were lots of boats of all shapes and sizes. There were sailboats, small fishing boats, speedboats, and some big yachts.

As Juan, Jessie, and Grandad set out across the water, several large manatees swam below.

They were feeding on seaweed. The adult manatees were as large as cows. The manatees stayed close to shore and every few minutes they came to the surface to breathe. The manatees didn't understand they were in danger from so many boats.

Juan spotted something big in the water. "Wow," he said. "Look at that big fish!"

"That's not a fish, Juan," said Grandad. "That's a sea cow."

Juan laughed. "You must be kidding, Grandad," he said. "I know cows don't live in the sea."

"Well, it's not exactly a cow," said Grandad. "It's called a manatee and it's really more like a big seal. Manatees can weigh as much as Grandma's car and they live here in the warm water."

Just then the boat bounced and swayed. There was a loud ka-thud!

"Great rolling thunder! What was that?" said Grandad. "We must have hit something big!"

He quickly turned the engine off.

Chapter 3
Blood in the Water

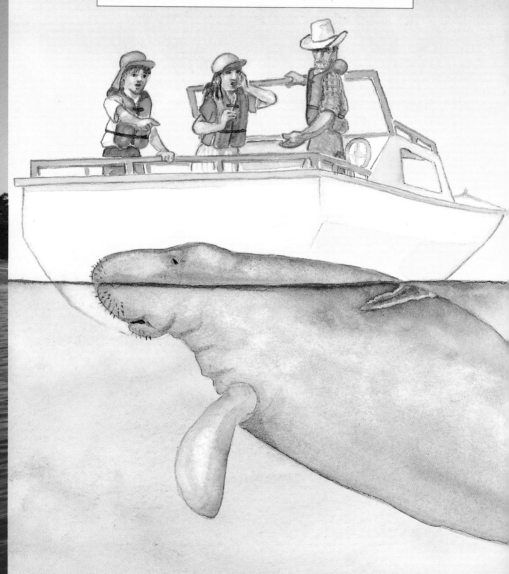

Jessie rushed to the side of the boat. But she couldn't see anything. Juan ran to the back of the boat and looked over the side.

"The water is all red," he yelled, "I think it looks like blood!"

Jessie went back to have a look. "There's a manatee, Grandad," she screamed, "I think we've hit a manatee!"

The manatee was stunned and dazed. The boat had struck its head. The propeller had cut a deep gash in its back. The manatee was losing lots of blood. Jessie felt sick and Juan looked very pale.

Grandad said, "We have to call for help." He grabbed the radio.

He called the Coast Guard and told them where they were. "Get a rescue boat out here fast," he said. "We've just hit a manatee."

Just then Juan yelled out, "I can see a little manatee, it must be her baby!"

Grandad told the Coast Guard about the baby. "Please hurry," said Grandad, "the mother manatee is cut very badly."

Grandad slowly moved the boat closer to the hurt manatee.

"If we'd been going more slowly, I might have seen her in time," he said.

Jessie began to cry. Juan didn't say anything, he just watched the little manatee swimming beside its mother.

Chapter 4
Manatee Rescue

When the Coast Guard rescue boat arrived the manatee was nowhere to be seen. Juan thought she must be dead.

One of the men on the Coast Guard rescue boat told Juan manatees can stay under water for 15 minutes before coming up for air.

Suddenly Jessie yelled, "I can see the baby manatee! It's over there!"

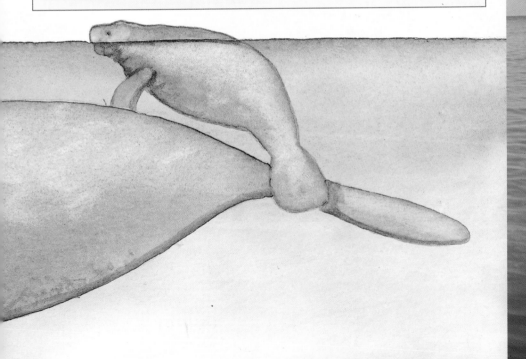

The rescue boat moved carefully towards the baby. When they were close, the mother manatee appeared. The rescuers quickly tossed a net around her. The manatee tried to get away, but the rescuers opened the back of the special rescue boat. The rescuers gently pulled the injured manatee into the boat.

But they couldn't leave the baby behind. Without its mother it would die. One of the rescuers jumped into the water and wrapped a small net around the baby. They lifted it onto the boat and put it with its mother.

"Thanks folks," said the Coast Guard, "we'll take them to a place where they take care of injured sea animals, and we'll see if they can help her."

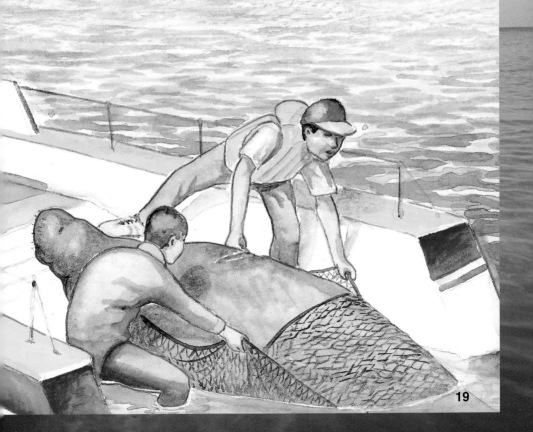

19

Chapter 5
The End of the Holiday

Juan and Jessie were very quiet. They weren't sure they wanted to go fishing anymore.

Grandad said, "How about we forget about fishing today. Let's go home now."

Juan looked at the Coast Guard rescue boat moving away. "Do you know where they're going Grandad? Can we go there, too?"

"Yes," said Jessie, "I want to see if the manatee is going to be all right."

Grandad thought that was a great idea. He started up the engine and soon they were following the Coast Guard rescue boat. But this time Grandad drove much more slowly, and Jessie and Juan kept watch for manatees.

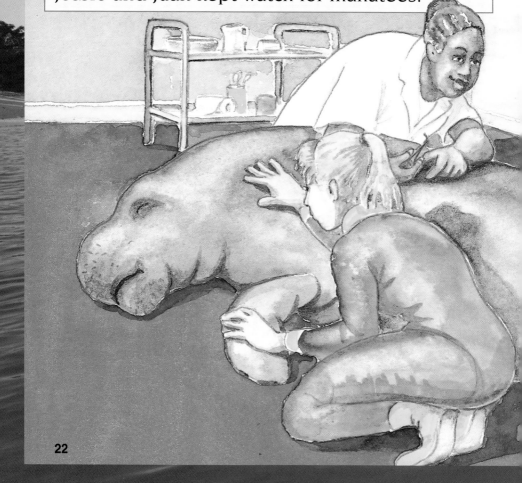

When they arrived at the hospital for injured sea animals, Grandad took them inside. Juan saw one of the men from the Coast Guard rescue boat talking to a vet.

Grandad went and asked them how the manatee was.

"It's too soon to tell," said the vet. "If you come back again tomorrow, I should have some more news about her."

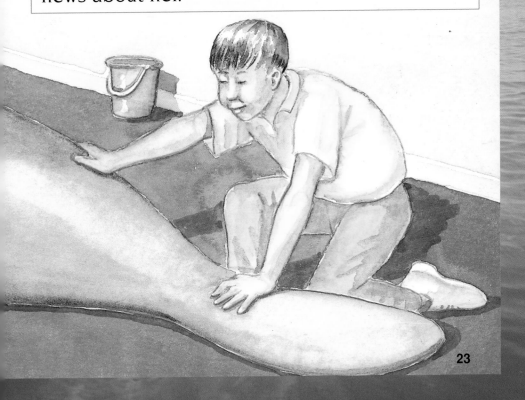

23

Juan, Jessie and Grandad worried about the manatee and her baby all night. When they went back the next morning, the vet took them to see the injured manatee. She was resting well and her cut was healing. The vet told them she was going to be fine.

As they headed home, Juan said, "This is one fishing trip we'll never forget!"

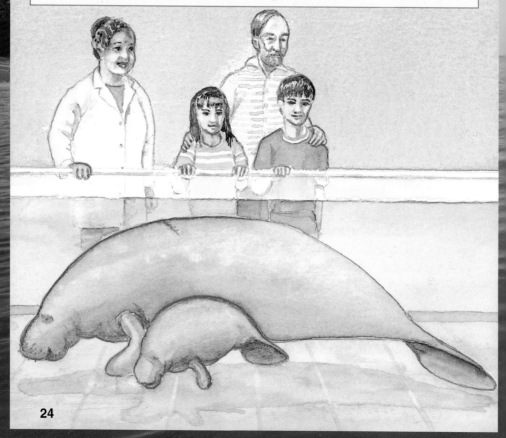